CF: For Georgia, Jago and Isla.

JB: For Sam and Alice

The Gratitude Stone

Charlotte Fincken & Jake Biggin

Douglas Dragon and his young friend Ernie sat together on their favourite rock.

As they gazed dreamily across the lush, green valley, Ernie rested his head on the soft, green scales of his friend's tail.

Ernie looked up at Douglas and asked softly,

"I have a funny feeling in my tummy. Can you feel it too?"

Douglas shook his head kindly,

"Can you explain what it feels like? Perhaps I can help."

"I'll try. It's right here, under my heart",

Ernie explained, pointing to his chest.

"It feels like it's empty. A bit like your food bowl!"

Douglas laughed as he curled his tail protectively around Ernie's waist.

"I think you are feeling sad my friend and maybe a little bit worried. I have an idea, so trust me and climb carefully onto my back. Hold on tight!"

Ernie felt a leap of excitement in his chest as they soared through the sky towards his home.

Over the green valley they travelled until they
landed with a bump on the roof of the treehouse at
the end of his garden.

"Okay", said Douglas boldly, "take a good look at your home, your family and everything that belongs to you".

"I'm looking Douglas", said Ernie slightly impatiently, "but I'm not sure how this will stop my tummy feeling funny".

Douglas pulled something out from his patchwork satchel.

It was a smooth, curved stone about the size of Ernie's hand and it seemed to be almost alive with words!

"This is my Gratitude Stone", said Douglas proudly as he held it high in the air. Ernie was impressed.

"Why is it covered in words? Did you find it on the beach like that?" He ran his finger over the stone and looked up at Douglas expectantly.

"These are my gratitudes Ernie. The things in my life that I feel grateful for every morning as I wake and every evening as the sun goes down. I say thank you for these things, however big or small they are"

Ernie frowned. "But why write them on this stone
when you could just remember them?"

Douglas smiled at his friend.

"Because I need to remember to remember. In other words, I am a little forgetful. Having the pictures of my mind written onto the surface of my Gratitude Stone helps me to remember to say 'Thank you.'"

Ernie stared thoughtfully into the distance for a moment and then jumped to his feet.
"Back in a sec", he shouted as he clambered down from the treehouse at great speed.

Douglas chuckled to himself and closed his eyes as he rested his head against an ancient, gnarly branch.

After what seemed like a few short minutes, Ernie reappeared with a bundle of things stuffed into his pockets. He pulled out a pen, a scrap of paper, a smooth, white stone from Mum's plant pot and some biscuits!

Concentrating hard, Ernie began to write.

As the words began to appear, Ernie's smile grew wider and his eyes twinkled brightly.

"Thank you for my Mummy and Daddy and thank you for my sister Gracie, who makes me smile inside even when she is being annoying.

Thank you for my tree house that Grandad built.
Oh, and thank you for Grandad."

Douglas wrapped his tail around Ernie's waist again, his heart full of love. The two friends sat together, ate biscuits and watched the orange sun as it began to close its eyes.

Out of the corner of his eye, Douglas noticed his friend clutching the stone close to his chest and asked,

"So, my friend, have you worked out the secret yet?"

Ernie held his stone up towards the setting sun.

"Being thankful every day helps the sad thoughts to fly away!"

The friends hugged, knowing that feeling happy was so easy when you knew how.

The End

Here's how you can sprinkle some gratitude on your day

- Find a calm place

- Close your eyes

- Take some lovely deep breaths

- Think about all the things that make you happy and say,

'Thank you'.

How to make a Gratitude Stone

- Find a stone that you love
- Paint it using your 'happy' colours
- Wait for it to dry
- Use a sharpie to write the things you are most thankful for
- Hold it close to your heart every day

Ideas for Gratitude

- Thank you for cuddles
- Thank you for sunsets
- Thank you for my best friend
- Thank you for my precious Grandpa who always plays with me
- Thank you for my Mummy who is always so kind
- Thank you for my daddy who is so proud of me
- Thank you for my healthy body

Printed in Great Britain
by Amazon